Menopause on the Mountain

N. S. Burdette

Menopause on the Mountain

(Ozark Life book 2)

N. S. Burdette

Menopause on the Mountain

In the kitchen is where I love to be.

I may be a bit old school and enjoy making traditional meals (insert eye roll here) but it honestly does make me happy. I am totally at home in the kitchen and love keeping my husband and family well fed.

Baking is another vice I have (my husband says it's a curse because he is the Guinea pig on all my creations).

Give me sugar, flour, a smidge of butter and I swear you will be making the "O" face before the timer goes off.

Banana bread is my new specialty, chocolate chip banana bread specifically. The smell of this splendid creation alone has been known to pack on a couple pounds (that's my story and I am sticking to it).

Back to the issue at hand.......

As I bend over the hot oven to check on the mother of all things yummy banana bread, I begin a little deep thinking (I find myself doing this a lot these days).

I have a huge to do list and there just isn't enough time in the day, even with my newly acquired retirement status.

All of the sudden, my body breaks out in burning hot fire.

What in the heck is going on?

This inferno isn't coming from the oven, it's coming from my head and spreading like wild fire down to my toes!

What in all things feminine is happening here?

Where the hell is the Judy Bloom book for this?

Isn't Margaret entering menopause by now? I could really use this book.

We grew up reading the books that prepared us for scoliosis, periods, big first times and the other milestones young girls endure.

Where is she now when I need her the most?

Hot flashes (what the hell purpose does that serve and dear lord why do they come at inopportune times?)!

Night sweats (in the middle of summer are you kidding me?)!

Mood swings (I swear if one more med alert commercial comes on I am throwing the tv)!

Chin hair (apparently you begin to lose hair on your head and sprout it on your face)!

My hormones are raging,
Or jumping ship.
The mood swings are plenty,
I despise this shit.
Menopause is evil,
I am not a fan.
Praying my next life,
Brings me back as a man.
I will seriously take,
The spontaneous erection.
To avoid this hormonal,
Demonic affliction.

I am so over this hormone hell and it's only just begun! This crazy new life does not afford me time to deal with all this!

I have errands to run, grandkids to spoil, parents to nag.......gahhhhhh!

Enough of this hormonal pity party already, my timer just went off!

With the warm banana bread out of the oven it's time to get out and make a trip to mom and dads.

Maybe the fresh air will do me some good. Dad is my absolute best taste tester in all things baked goods so I decide to take him a warm loaf.

My parents live about 20 minutes down the mountain and near the beautiful White River. It is so peaceful and picturesque that visitors come often. So it is definitely relaxing to make this trip.

I make it down to mom and dads in time to get entertained (or enlightened, whichever).

Mom is busy complaining about dad using a new product they ordered through the mail (they do this a lot these days).

My mother is the queen of all things mail order.

No online shopping for this woman, no sir.

Mom gets multiple catalogs in the mail each day along with boxes of her mail order treasures.

Anyway, Dad had apparently asked mom to help him apply this mole removal miracle on his skin tags and wanted them ALL done.

It seems when it came to the one on his thigh, mom refused.

I am both intrigued and scared shitless as to where this is going. Knowing mom this is going to get interesting fast.

Mom gives me a look of "I am serious and you better not mess with me" (she seriously has perfected that look) when she simply says "I am not putting that there, it's too close to your tallywacker!"

KILL ME NOW!

Mom continues on with "that's all I need is for you to get up in the middle of the night to pee and have it fall into the toilet!"

"You would probably flush it!"

Oh my god, this is my life now!

I am certain the heat in my face this time is not hot flash related!

That is my cue to drop and run, when parents begin with tallywacker talk it is time to vacate the premises.

I back out of the dining room and make my way to the door as dad explains to mom "it isn't even close to that".

Yup, time to pick up my pace.

These two have always had just the cutest banter. I love the relationship they have but when it takes the dark tallywacker turn, its time for this girl to go.

I make it home in time to clean up a major toy explosion from the night before and start dinner (I am a domestic marvel like that).

All of this before I have to take off again and head into town to pick the boys up from school (we have stepped in to help raise our two grandsons for some time, Ryland age 9 and Declan age 7 who was also diagnosed at age 2 with autism). Once everyone is fed and homework is done we can finally relax.

We settle in to a little family time that includes movies and popcorn, life is good.

We are about 45 minutes into Deadpool 2 when Declan comes running into the den (He was watching Toy Story in the living room, trust me Deadpool vocabulary is not something Mountain View Elementary is ready for).

Anyway, Declan yells "Papa there's a cow in the yard!". It is completely black outside (8:30pm) so it's impossible to see anything through the window. I am thinking "great who left the gate open" just as Bob says "I know I shut and latched that gate".

Holy shit!

It's got to be the bear! (we had a bear incident a few weeks ago that will haunt me for life).

Bears eat people and a bear in my yard is cause for concern or total breakdown, whatever.

Declan breaks into my meltdown with "cow in the yard, I am gonna get it!"

Dear mother of god!

Declan shoots out the front door while I am chasing and screaming for him to stop!

Bob has, at this point, made it outside and is catching Declan when I hit the porch (just another example of why Bob is my hero- most days).

I swear to everything holy that I thought I was going to have a heart attack!

Once on the porch Bob, Ryland, Declan and I look out into the yard (preparing for a Yogi visit) when we see ...... several sets of bovine eyes staring at us!

Oh my freaking shit!

Ok, there was no bear...whew!

But how in the hell did that many cows get into the yard? And why in the hell are they pooping next to my porch?

Bob hops on Old Red (the go to quad when time is of the essence) and starts to chase the cows. Realizing there is no opening for said bovine invaders to escape (since Bob did in fact close the gate), Bob flies past the wayward herd so he can get to the gate first.

Once at the gate Bob un hooks and opens the gate to get them back into the field.

That was our sign to get the boys ready for bed because this Nana needed a cocktail.

There isn't one day or one moment in this new retirement life that doesn't require a level of sedation. Let's see the commercial for that in the AARP ad.

As the sun came up over the mountain in the morning Bob was out looking for the perimeter breach and running more fence.

Of course he had to go all NCIS on this to determine his plan of attack, he is a man after all.

The cows braved the holler to eat our freshly mowed grass and drop fertilizer bombs everywhere as they ate.

Nothing could have prepared me for this abundance of recycled grass or the odiferous impact it would have on my senses.

I remember when the biggest issue I had were squirrels digging in my window boxes. The struggle is real kids, very real!

Lord give me strength!

I decide that sitting on the deck, drinking coffee while watching Bob run fence out back is my happy place this morning. Some days you just need a little caffeine and sunshine to appreciate life and today was no exception.

That is until Ryland comes running outside, in full panic mode, screaming about something important.

Apparently there is a lizard in the house and I absolutely need to get it and fast. (sigh)

These moments never stop or even pause, just one moment rolling into the next. I know there was a point in my life that all this mayhem is retribution for and it's probably deserved but....... good gravy!

I ask the adorable child where he saw the lizard and he tells me " kitchen!" in his I am freaking out voice.

This all makes sense, I have been telling Declan all morning long to close the patio doors so we could avoid this very issue.

I really need to apologize to my mom on my next visit down the mountain. I know these boys are nothing compared to the hell I put my parents through growing up.

I get into the kitchen and ask Ryland "where is it?", he tells me it "ran under the fridge"!
The whole time I am silently praying it is in fact a lizard and not a snake (I really hate snakes).

Dear lord in heaven, I am praying there is a lizard in my kitchen!
My former self is shaking her head with a little palm to face action.

Ok, now I need something to slide under the fridge and coax the lizard out so the reptile can be set free.
These cute little blue tailed lizards are harmless but can lose their tails if you aren't careful and I am not up for "operation tail search".

I head to the garage for the needed supplies. I need to scoot the little guy out to freedom without causing any tail trauma.

Never in my life did I ever think I would be spending my days in the Ozarks chasing lizards from my kitchen, but hey, I am here and living it.

So now I have a long piece of Formica from the garage in one hand and a prayer in the other. I kneel down, on all 4's to sweep the lizard out from his hiding spot.

Ryland has a plastic bucket and a deep desire to eradicate the lizard. Ryland assures me he is ready to catch it...perfect.

As I sweep the plastic out towards Ryland and his bucket, the baby lizard scurries out.

This lizard is barely 2 inches long, so catching it should be simple, note- I said **should be**.

At this point, I yell for Ryland to "catch it" but of course he can't hear me due to the fact he is releasing the highest, longest blood curdling scream I have ever heard!

So now I have to jump up (truly not as graceful as it sounds) and try to catch the little guy because Ryland is having a moment.

As I get close to baby Elton (yes I have named him, at this point because if we do not catch him he will be a new dependent) he scurries toward Ryland causing him to release another ear shattering scream and drop his bucket!

Dear lord!

This boy is going to have a heart attack if this lizard isn't released back into the wild fast.

I get the 2 inch lizard to run to the patio doors and yell for Ryland to open them so Elton can leave the house. Ryland is shaking in fear but grabs the door handle while climbing onto a chair and opens the door (success, teamwork, small goals).

The lizard finally leaves and there is no one more relieved than Ryland.

I look at Ryland and ask "all better now?"

He turns to me with a look of horror and says "I need to go to the bathroom, I think I just peed"!

God help him if he gets up close and personal with an armadillo!

Is it Monday yet?

I need some me time........

It would seem "me time" is code for please call my name non stop.

The boys were unbelievably needy for absolutely no reason today. Every time I left a room I would hear, "Nana, can you get me? Nana, can I have? Nana, Nana, Nana". I am blessed beyond belief to have grandchildren and I love them like crazy but I was just about done for the day.

At one point Bob and I were on the porch watching the boys bowling on the sidewalk when the ball rolled toward the hollar. I looked at Bob and simply said "Aww hell no!" Just about the time I hear "Nana" not even waiting for the sentence to finish coming out of their mouth I yelled "I changed my name".

I think Bob liked this game because he told the boys my name was now George.

I figure, that's good lets run with it.

Of course Ryland was not about to play along but Declan found this spectacular.

Declan began calling me George from that moment on. It was adorable to hear "George, I need 1,2 corndogs" or "George, I need your help". He knew I was Nana but he was having a lot of fun so I went with it.

I was George for days and Declan never faltered.

It was all fun until it was time for school pick up.

You see we drive the boys to school daily and pick them up when school is out. Ryland gets dropped off first and we wait with Declan for his teacher or aide to come out and pick him up. I get a little Declan time to play games or listen to music he likes before he goes into school. It's key to maintain a routine with Declan because he does not respond well to change.

At 2:30 I made my way back to school to pick up the boys.

I pulled up to the loading area where both boys were ready and waiting. The boys are brought to the jeep by Declan's teacher.

Declan's teacher is amazing and I will praise this woman until my dying breath.

Today when Mrs. Brewer opened the door to the jeep, Declan looked up at me completely excited (I pick them up daily so I was a little surprised at his enthusiasm). Declan has the biggest smile on his face and says "George! It's so good to see you today!"

Oh no!

Now his teacher is looking at me with clear confusion on her face and all I can do is smile. There are a line of cars behind me waiting to pick up their children but I know I have to explain. I frantically explain that Bob told the boys I changed my name to George because they kept calling me.

I felt the look of judgement coming and was totally prepared to grovel so I could pull away. To my surprise Mrs. Brewer smiled and said "well ok Ms. George, we'll see you tomorrow".

See, this woman is amazing!

I decide to make good use of our 20 minute drive home and advise Declan I changed my name back to Nana. I envisioned the next Walmart bathroom trip and Declan asking George (me) to take him into the woman's restroom. That would bring on a whole new batch of questions I am not prepared for.

Game over!

Labor Day had snuck up on us so we took the day to work on an electric gate. We decided with all of natures invaders an electric gate is a good call.

I will be honest here, I was pretty tired of "getting the gate" because of course I prefer Bob drive everywhere. If you have ever had to get out of a warm vehicle in the rain to open a driveway gate and wait to close and latch it, you can understand the importance of a remote control to do it for you.

Running electric lines under ground doesn't sound too bad, dig a trench, run some pipe and feed the wire....gravy right?

Unless you live on an Ozark mountain where there is no dirt and every swing of a pick throws sparks into the air.

Yup, we have 100 feet to dig and 2.3 acres of solid rock to do it in.

Labor Day will in fact go down as Hard Labor Day for the greater good.

Hours of pick swinging, rock throwing, spade scooping and we are blessed with a trench that isn't necessarily great but will work for what we need.

Lots of work in the hot sun and we are in the home stretch. I can see the remote gate in my near future and I am beyond excited.

This is my life now, my 20 year old self would "mean girl" all over the me of today.

My days of dining, shopping and socializing are just memories and a remote gate has me giddy like its Christmas morning.

At no point in my life did I envision the path that led me to the here and now. But here I am, only now I have a remote controlled gate (picture happy dance if you must but I assure you it isn't pretty).

The week rolls by with homework, housework and cooking. School is going well for the little guys. We are bear free and the cows are keeping their distance. It's the little things that keep me going.

Wednesday arrives and so does the local fair.

The boys are excited to be going to the fair because they have rides and all things fair related. After waiting in a long hot line to get arm bands the boys are ready to tear up the rides.

I walked with the boys and Ryland's best friend Eli around the fair while Bob checked out the talent show on the stage. I watched as they road every single ride at least 6 times. Praying they could burn off a little energy (go me!).

I was ready to head home after a couple hours but the boys had other plans as more of their friends arrived.

I was chasing kids from ride to ride and walking what felt like hundreds of miles. This is far too much exercise for this Nana but the boys were happy (ahhh, the sacrifices we make for our grandkids).

After 4.5 hours of food, rides and livestock viewing we actually got to take the boys home.

We had just enough time to get them in the shower and bed before 10:00pm on a school night-yikes!

The morning did not go well but was definitely better than I was prepared for.

I got 2 days of quiet to catch up on laundry, vacuuming and bed making before the crazy weekend began.

When in the world did I go from living for the weekend to praying for the weekday?

Oh yeah, when I hit 50 and Mother Nature bitch slapped me with my new reality!

Yeah, good times........

Bob and I decided to take the boys to get winter type school clothes on the weekend. The weather is in no way fall or winter ready but this is all about being prepared. When you have to drive 2 plus hours to find a Target or Old Navy we decided we would go all in. Obviously that meant leaving by 8:30 in the morning to get a full day of school clothes shopping in with these adorable boys.

Let me start with, Declan is a foody and a picky one at that.

In my defense, my Nana brain did not get her morning java so an epic snack failure occurred in the process of this outing. I failed to pack the emergency goldfish which, according to Mrs. Brewer, is equivalent to Declan's morning coffee (this was a huge mistake).

At 10:15 Declan saw a Burger King and lost his shit!

He promptly told Papa he had to turn around and even threw in a "Can I please get Burger King, I am so hungry...pretty please" (didn't they eat breakfast just 3 hours ago?).

After several attempts to get him to wait failed, we found ourselves pulling into a Burger King at 10:20 in the morning.

I am not even sure it would have been a good idea at noon but Declan said pretty please so here we are.

The manager was kind enough to allow us to order lunch and the boys got to attack the, and I quote, "best playland on the planet".

I will put this in the win column.

At least they would not be hangry while shopping (hungry, angry shopping is never a good idea........... ever).

This little sidetrack may work out in my favor after all.

Several hours of Ryland trying on everything in his size and style (he is freaking 9 and has a style?) we emerge with pants!

Ryland is unbelievably picky so this is a huge win. Declan was cool with everything but in love with his new underwear (Declan rarely wears clothes at home so it's all about underwear). Oh and let's not forget the Doggie Doo game that made it into the cart- who makes up these games? I am sure we will be subjected to this game for a long time to come and of course Declan was happy.

So after hours of walking around the fair with them Wednesday and then marathon shopping Saturday I earned a little couch surf time and recovery day, didn't I?

Yeah, dilutions are also common with my new hormone struggle, clearly!

I forgot what it was like having little guys around 24/7.

With the school year and lots of kids sharing germs it's a guarantee your house will be subjected to "the crud" at least once a year. Ours was no exception and the germs kissed both boys but of course not at the same time.

So today Ryland had a follow up with the doctor from the most recent kiss of crud that included an ear infection. As we are waiting to be seen Ryland and I are working on his homework in the waiting area.

The office is busy with a lot of "older" adults (oh crap, I could officially be included in that category- sigh) and Ryland is being an absolute angel (this is rare for this little stinker).

When the nurse called him, we had to pack up and head into the back. We followed the nurse into the exam room while the she reviewed the ER visit details and offered Ryland a bag of sour gummies.

This is after school appointment so a snack is cool and he was doing really well.

When the doctor came into the room he started in on small talk with Ryland about the shot he got in his bottom and then starts in on the exam.

The doctor talked about dart guns and how they have changed since he was a kid and all the good toy stuff. He gets down on the kids level which really comforts them. Ryland really likes his new doctor so of course I love him too.

Especially when he told Ryland he had the best Nana in Stone County....ummm yeah I am (seriously, I am).

The doctor decides to give it another week for the tonsil concern (little swollen still but look fine). He tells Ryland he is good to go unless he starts feeling yucky again, then he'll need us to come back (Ryland not happy with the potential return or more medicine).

To soften the blow the doctor asks Ryland if candy will make it better, Ryland replies with a very curt "no".

He asks if a fruit snack will make it better, Ryland replies again with a very annoyed "no".

The doctor finally says will a moon pie make it better?

Wait, what?
Umm........ did someone just say moonpie?

Ryland asks "what is a moonpie?"

The doctor looks at me with complete shock, like I just dropped an F bomb in church or something far more heinous!

I think I just lost my Stone County Nana crown in this conversation.

How could I be any kind of Nana and not have given these boys a moonpie?

I am questioning my own Nana abilities at this very moment. Dear lord what else have I failed them on?

While I am dissecting my Nana fails, the doctor comes back in the room with a slew of treats and one monster double moon pie.

I repeat a DOUBLE MOONPIE!

I never knew one existed!

This doctor has just proven that no matter how much life we live, we do in fact not know it all!

We left the office with enough treats to embarrass the best Halloween haul.

Long story short....

Ryland not a fan of moon pie's (no idea how this happened). Of course this Nana had to steal a bite, purely for nostalgia purposes.

I have to say it has been about 40 years since I have had a single moonpie but this little treat will now be in my menopause emergency kit.

Lord have mercy.....moonpies, menopause and moscato.....hey, that has the makings of a great country song.

I am humming it right now!

The morning comes and both boys are ready for school. We step out onto the porch to get in the Jeep to make the 20 minute drive to town when Ryland yells "Declan's bike is broken".

Pretty sure he was riding it after dinner last evening so I decide to inspect the area. Sure enough the bike is lying on its side and the seat is shredded into several pieces all over the front yard.

Immediately I am in "the freaking bear is back" mode!

Something attempted to eat the seat off a 7 year olds bike while we all slept! I was fast asleep in my house while the wild beast of the human eating kind was feasting just 20 feet from my front door! I am cursing the paddle door knob decision as that realization set in.

I am going to lose my mind!

When I frantically relay the story to Bob he quickly squashes my fears with "it was probably just a raccoon".
Just a raccoon, really?

Ok, did you see The Great Outdoors?
Do you know what those mask wearing Devils can do? They are stealth like demons with little sharp fingers and can get in from anywhere.
Not much better than the bear scenario but Bob is trying.

Bob now must add bike repair man to his long list of skills. A seven year old needs a bike like I need moscato and that folks is serious!

New seat was installed before the boys made it home from school.

Crisis averted!

We finished up dinner and retreated to the den. About the same time Declan comes running in yelling "there's a bear in the yard! I am going upstairs, you going to shoot it papa?"

WHAT????

I jump up, panic setting in and look in the yard to see a small "bear" doing what appears to be "the floss" on all 4's.

Upon close inspection the bear is clearly a 9 year old in a gorilla costume. I should be overjoyed that these two are playing as one team and not fighting like they are in the octagon.

I am however more concerned with the dual plotting to create mischief that came so easily to them. They are 7 and 9 so we have at least a decade of training exercises to live through. The 9 year old ringleader who put his little brother up to the ruse has mad skills and yes, I am afraid.

Papa decides to turn the tables on the pranksters and runs outside holding a pellet gun in the air.

Ryland jumps up with hands in the air like he was just busted robbing a bank yelling, "it's just me Papa!" while laughing his little butt off.

I am surrounded by comedians.

A little while later we get called to the porch for yet another "bear" sighting (Declan apparently suited up to scare us too)........gahhh, these kids are just little shits!

And then I turned 52!

The boys were out with their mom so all was quiet on the mountain. Bob and I just finished putting away a truck load of groceries and were rocking on the porch enjoying the evening. We watched squirrels gathering fallen acorns, scurrying across the lawn. As we are discussing the miracles of nature and retirement, we see 2 majestic deer wander up to feast on fallen chestnuts.

Everything about this moment was so calming.

As the deer made their way up to the house we sat and watched trying to avoid making any noises. The last thing we wanted to do was spook them. Enjoying the scene from afar was rewarding enough.

As the deer made their way around the house and out of our line of vision I decided I wasn't done observing them.

I got up slowly from my rocking chair (total retirement vibe going on). I tip toed around the side of the house, walking in the direction the deer just traveled.

As I reach the corner of the house I see one of the deer in the distance grazing on the tall grass and some grapes I had thrown out earlier.

It was breathtaking to see.

While I was enjoying my majestic view, movement to my left caught my attention.

I turned my head slowly in time to see deer number one (who I clearly missed) on his back legs grunting wildly. He began pounding the ground and making what is best described as a charging bull sound!

My instinct SHOULD have been to head back to the porch and Bob, but I froze.

I began picturing the movie Tommy Boy when the deer attacked David Spade and Chris Farley. I pictured all sorts of scenarios that did not involve keeping my pretty smile intact.

This guy did not want an audience and he was letting me know!

As the deer began to jump and stomp in a circle I figured that was my only warning before he went all Muhammad Ali on me. I turned and ran back to the porch hoping the deer went the opposite direction.

When I reached the porch, Bob (who is oblivious to the near fatal assault I just evaded) asks "where did they go?"

I think my blank stare should have been enough to answer him but I decided to share with my soulmate the horror of my brush with nature.

Before I even finish with the scary details, my hero, the man I have worshipped for the better part of 36 years begins to laugh. Not a simple body shaking chuckle but a full on belly laugh that makes his eyes leak!

I am clearly unprepared for the creatures that surround me, husband included!

I also think nature is best observed through the window or at the zoo. The last thing I want to explain to the ER Doctor is how I lost my teeth to a Bambi attack.

Life in my new reality is never going to be boring.

I can feel it in my bones.

On to picture day for the boys at school (raising grandkids, ahhhhh) I was excited but they were just.....meh.

Not only was it picture day but Ryland had an eye Dr. appt. and then it was conferences at the school.

How did I survive this stuff with our kids?

Oh, and we had to run to the dump (because trash pick up doesn't happen out yonder).

Bob and I also climbed on the roof and tuck-pointed one of the fireplace chimneys.

Whew, right?

Well anyway, back to my main subject.....

On Monday Ryland had a spot on his cheek (huge panic because it was picture week). I told him it was fine, we would put some Zapzyt on it and he would be fine for pictures.

Ryland then proceeds to ask me why he got a zit. I explained it probably wasn't a zit but the medicine would help heal the tiny dot.

Ryland, of course isn't satisfied with my medical skills.

Now he is more adamant than ever he has pimples and that he is in fact entering puberty (he is 9 and actually said puberty..oh god!).

I tell him it isn't puberty and it's one tiny dot, smaller than the head of a pin.

He continues with his stubborn stance ......

"Look Nana, I have a zit! I am starting to get a mustache and I think I have hair in my armpit...that's puberty!"

Holy shit!

I look at him while biting my cheeks so I don't laugh hysterically and explain.....

"That is not a zit its a dot, that is a freckle in your armpit and you do not have a mustache, I have a mustache and yours isn't even close to dusting a cookie (menopause is a cruel bitch)!

Please god help me survive the day when he actually hits the big P-word because I will definitely be sending him to Papa for that talk.

How am I not prepared for all this?

I grew up in a house of 8 children, 8 children in one house and we raised 3 of our own!

I have to give serious props to my parents who were unbelievably great to all of us. We were a handful and tested them often. They survived, we survived and definitely learned from it.

We once decided to visit my sister Tammie and her children in California. I was in 8th grade at the time, it was cold in Illinois and California sounded so exciting.

So my older sister (Vickie), myself and 2 younger brothers (John and Rick) loaded up in the Maverick with mom and dad at the helm and started our drive. Seriously, my dad drove from Illinois to California with 4 kids (our 3 older siblings were too busy being adults to come along) for Easter break.

It was going to be a great vacation.

Driving southern states there and northern states back, the scenery alone was worth the trip.

We got to visit Disney Land and went to Hollywood where I got my 8th grade graduation dress.

We saw the ocean and got to spend time with our tiny nephew and nieces. We took one day and went to Mexico where we picked up lots of souvenirs.

It was a long day of shopping the markets and enjoying things we had never experienced.

The trip out of Mexico was pretty uneventful until we reached the border on our way back to San Diego.

Let me start with this.......

My mother is of German decent with olive skin and jet black hair. Now in the US this wasn't anything big but while trying to enter a foreign border it proved a little interesting.

As we crossed the walkway through Mexico to California we were asked our names and for any ID, once provided we were allowed to pass. When it came time for mom to pass they asked her the same questions but mom had an ear infection and couldn't hear them and just kept saying "what?".

This posed a problem as I think the border guards took it as mom didn't comprehend English (not good, and I was beginning to panic).

Dad stepped forward and said "Nancy, tell them your name and where you're from" to which the guards responded with "step back sir!".

Now there are 4 kids standing here watching our parents try to get back into the US so we can go home and mom is apparently drawing attention.

My sister Vickie, being a complete pain in the ass, starts yelling "Maria, Maria, tell them your name!" while laughing hysterically.

I think my dad wanted to kill all of us, because we all started laughing at that point. Clearly he did not see the humor of the situation that 4 rambunctious kids did.

Eventually mom was released without incident and we were able to get to our car and leave.

I have to say, I haven't been to Mexico since (not taking any chances that they remember us).

So why I am so unprepared for this new life is beyond me, my childhood should have made this look easy.

Alas, I will spend a lifetime trying to figure out when I broke the giant mirror....

Bob and I spent the morning working on some tree trimming. There were (take note of past tense) shrubs next to our deck that were out of control. The shrubs were a beautiful green with shiny leaves and really full but the leaves were like razor blades.

If you brushed against it or touched it you better have lots of Curad on hand.

As we are trimming and bleeding, I decide I want them pulled out. There is only so much pricking one can tolerate. They were really ticking me off and I was tired of getting stabbed. So Bob, being my hero (most days) wrapped a chain around the shrub and hooked it up to the truck.

We had gotten a lot of rain so the ground should be soft, hence releasing the roots pretty easily.

A few attempts and the shrubs hadn't even moved an inch.

Change of plans....

Bob breaks out the chainsaw and we start cutting away at this beast. As I am pulling branches I pull my shirt sleeves over my hands (because I didn't want to go in the house and grab my gloves-big mistake).

Things are moving along well, I have amassed a significant pile of limbs and was feeling pretty impressed with myself. Of course I hadn't even gotten my arm up to pat myself on the back when Bob says ....."that's full of poison ivy!".

Umm, WHAT?

I think, at this point, Bob is really just messing with me because I did not listen to his "put gloves on" demand. Now my mind starts forming the "get even" plot for my evil husband. Of course I don't need gloves, I am toughening up and adapting to my surroundings. He is just being a pain, always trying to get me to fall for his shenanigans.

Momentarily I think he may actually have my best interest at heart so I look at the very large pile of greenery.

OH MY SHIT!

Not only do I see that I am an overachiever but there are poisonous vines all over the pile I stacked!

This little revelation would have been more helpful a couple hours ago!

Deep breath........

Don't panic, people survive this all the time.

I finished up, went into the house and stripped off my infected clothes and dropped them in the washer.

Next step: A shower to rid myself of any potential poison ivy goo. After all, it is the sap that causes the reaction, right?

I jumped into the hot shower and soaped up the loofah like always and begin scrubbing my hands and arms, no poison ivy for this chick, no way. I am cleaning this stuff off my flesh like a boss!

Feeling pretty good about how quickly I was able to get in the shower I let my mind wander. Deep in thought about landscaping and planters I continue on with my shower and switch to normal shower mode. Without thinking I take the big soapy loofah and lather up my whole body.

Oh no, this is not good!

I just used the same ivy goo covered loofah and washed my entire body, my whole body...... including my bits!

Oh my god, I just washed my bits with the poison ivy covered loofah!

I feel it spreading all over me now!

I am going to have to go to the Dr. for poison ivy on my freaking bits and explain how it happened!

Gahhhhhh!

I quickly drop the loofah and start soaping up my entire body, bits included! Silently praying to God I will be spared from the seeping, blistering hell that is poison ivy!

When I exit the shower I frantically tell Bob what happened (he always calms me, always).

Bob looks at me and I see on his face he is preparing to release calming wisdom so I wait...... he freaking starts laughing!

This man has always been my rock and he just laughed!

This is a point in our relationship where I would plot my revenge but that would have to wait. I am freaking out about my blistering bits.

Once Bob has caught his breath and all laughter had ceased Bob tells me there is a 3 day incubation period before poison ivy will show up on my flesh.

Ummm......

Not sure when my husband became a botanists but I am pretty sure I feel the poison all over my skin.

Bob assures me (in his best empathetic voice) I should be fine.

That's it?

The calming wisdom of ....“you should be fine”!

These are my bits for gods sake....
MY FREAKING BITS!

I can't even begin to tell you what I envision the next 3 days will be like! I am certain Bob will have his doctorate in gynecology before the weekend is through.

Dr. Bob and I along with my bits will be waiting patiently for Monday (I have already checked the moscato supply and I think we need to make a wine run).

Bob was spared retaliation this time as the three days passed and bits were blister free. I can't help but think that God felt the need to spare me this horror only to save me for what has yet to come (holding my breath in anticipation I assure you).

After the whole poison-bit-gate we decided we had to run to Mountain Home to pick up things we can't get locally and wine (wine is one of my new staples in moderation of course thanks to the whole withering ovary thing).

Now this is an hour drive one way just to get beer/wine or boots (all of which are necessary to survive here- proven fact).

So we loaded up the boys and headed out with shopping list in hand to make this trip count.

Once we arrived at our first stop and started gathering the life sustaining essentials the boys declared they "are starving" and "need Wendys".

Now for little kids making this long ride they were being good and very helpful so we were ok with the little detour. We do not have access to Wendy's locally so it was quite the treat for them.

Once everyone was fed all things fried we headed back to the task at hand.

We spent about 4 hours gathering and loading the Jeep before we started the hour long trek back home.

I have told you all that, to share this.....

The radio station reception while traveling through the Ozark mountains is just horrible but we were lucky enough to find a classic rock station.

Now with 2 kids in tow classic rock is not a preferred listening treasure but I am a believer in expanding their horizons, so classic rock it is.

As we are listening I hear little voices singing in the back- very cool right?

I am feeling pretty good about this little trip. Happy boys, list filled and no fighting, this grand-parenting thing is going pretty smooth.

As we are all jamming to some Free Falling I hear Ryland belting out loud and proud " I'm free, free ballen".

What in the name of all things Petty was that?

Ryland is as proud as can be, enjoying himself and I am mortified!

The chorus comes back on and so does Ryland's rendition.

Ok, time to teach this child the true meaning of the words......

After a very lengthy debate Ryland is certain he is correct and I don't have the energy to fight him any longer.

I could take this as a grand-parenting fail but I am in fact putting this in the win column......they listened and enjoyed classic rock even if it was on their terms.

I however will never hear the song in my head correctly again.

Enjoy yourself the next time you listen to that song and try not to think about Ryland's loud and proud version, you are welcome!

Our days begin to take on a simple routine, wake up at 6am start my coffee (clearly, so no one is injured) and wake up our grandsons to get ready to meet the day. Lunches are packed, breakfasts are made and then the 20 minute drive to school.

When raising our children I never once considered the possibility that I would start the process all over with grandchildren.

Don't get me wrong, I love my grandsons with every fiber of my being and at 52 I think I can handle it.........

Until a hot flash kicks in at the very same time one demands a snack and the other needs math homework help and your husband asks "what's for dinner?".

If you have not had the pleasant experience of a hot flash in the Ozark fall (equivalent to Florida spring break temps I assure you) let me just say....bite it!

My body felt like lava and my feet were like the iceberg that took out the Titanic.

All those people whom I love unconditionally felt like a pool of piranha at feeding time! I am surrounded by testosterone so there is no chance in hell I will be provided sympathy or understanding. I can suck it up and multitask like a rock star or I can sneak off to the bathroom and stuff my face with chocolate until they notice I am gone.

Clearly the chocolate won out but that was actually the worst decision I could have made!

Did you know that caffeine can actually trigger a hot flash?

If you just answered yes, then you are dead to me!

I had absolutely no idea that the caffeine levels in chocolate can trigger the demons of menopause to poltergeist your body into the hell you spend your golden years avoiding! After discovering that little nugget of wisdom I decided to get my PHD in all things hormonal. Wine, dear god wine is a trigger, well alcohol actually but WINE?!

I have come to the conclusion that Mother Nature is definitely not a female because there is no way in hell a woman would knowingly project this upon another female being! Chocolate, wine and all things caffeine related can trigger your body to turn against you and set fire to your insides like a raging inferno! Sure there are drugs you can take to help replace your treacherous body but dear lord those side affects can create a pharmaceutical nightmare!

You can dye your hair, Botox your wrinkles and even have the fat sucked from your baby making pouch to ward off the aging process but there is no miracle that can save your hormones from packing up and moving on to greener pastures!

The only way to avoid this demonic overthrow of your all things feminine is to be born a male!

Pause for life events...........

We saw it fade,

The light in your eyes.

We felt you leaving,

Despite our cries.

The ache you endured,

To try to remain.

To keep us all hidden,

From your never ending pain.

We had you always,

No matter the cost.

Your presence no more,

The ultimate loss.

Your smile and laughter,

The memories remain.

Life without you,

Never the same.

We will go on,

Or face your wrath.

To spread your memory,

Along our new life path.

I never envisioned what it would require to pen an
obituary for the single most important woman in my
life.

My mother was an amazing woman and putting her
life on paper was by far the hardest thing I have ever
done. My strong, opinionated, pull no punches, love
you with her entire being mom lost her battle to cancer
today. Her life was so much more than words on
paper. She was so much to so many and everything to
even more. She was loved by all who met her. She
always told us god wasn't ready for her, the devil was
afraid she would take over and we believed her.

There isn't a soul on the planet that won't remember
something she said or did and smile. Mom was an
amazing inspiration to us all. She was the shoulder to
lean on, the biggest supporter to champion your cause
and your harshest critic when she needed to be. Mom
was fierce and loving, she was honest and funny. She
never let life slow her down. She taught us all to love
unconditionally, to forgive often, to see the funny in
the darkest of moments and most of all, never hold

back. She may have left this world but her presence will be felt forever in all of those she left behind. I am forever grateful that god chose her as my mom.

A small part of me takes comfort in the fact that she no longer struggles with the pain this horrible disease inflicted upon her. A larger part of me is heartbroken that the glue that held this giant crazy family together and functioning is gone. My father, our father lived to take care of our mom. I don't mean in the caretaker sense. I mean dads goal in life as far back as I can remember was loving all his children and part of that was loving our mom with every part of him. He worshipped her and always made sure she knew that she was his world. When mom left us, my thoughts were immediately shifted to my dad. How would he go on without her? I had never seen two people live as one like these two.

When I was younger I was certain I would never find a man who was as amazing as my dad. I wanted what mom had from the man I chose to spend my life with.

I am grateful that the moments we had growing up stayed with me. I will always be thankful that no matter how tough times were we never knew it. I will forever be grateful that the relationship my parents had, gave my 4 brothers guidance and my 3 sisters and I examples of what a perfect relationship is.

Lots of people say or even believe their parents are perfect but I have to say, our parents win that title, hands down.

Life will be a little duller without this crazy, loving little woman telling her stories to anyone who would listen. Not a day will pass that I won't smile about something she said or did.

I decided today I was going to take a little me time.

It was a sabbatical of sorts, to save my sanity. The boys were with their mom, Bob was working in the barn. I deserved a little me time so I was going all in.

When we built the mother of all barns Bob put a room in just for me. He created a she shed inside his man barn just for me. My she shed is equipped with air conditioning, a heated fireplace, a wine fridge as well as a futon and reading chair. Lest I forget, one vintage tanning bed for those moments I want to escape. In this whole aging process I have decided that rather than eliminate the ever present dimple thighs, I would bake them instead. Tan fat is way more appealing than white fat (this is my fantasy so if you know what is good for you, you will go with it).

Today I was going to spend fifteen minutes in that vintage cylinder of solitude and reflect on life while getting my fake bake on.

I fired up the radio to a smooth country station.

I spent a minute stripping down to the outfit I was born in.

I preheated the flesh oven so I didn't throw myself into cardiac arrest climbing in. I took a moment to inspect the surroundings. Even though my she shed is inside the barn I still make sure that there are no critters invading my space.

I put my eye protection in place and climbed on in. Ahhhhhhh...........

As I lay in my happy place I let my mind empty.

I was listening to the soothing words coming from Garth himself and just needed to breathe.

This is the calming peaceful minutes I needed. I started to fall into a light sleep just as I felt a light flutter against my thigh.

Ok, now I am awake!

In fact, I was bordering on a full panic mode.

I make the decision to shake my thigh assuming some lint or string fell off the towel I used to clean the bed. The light shake should be enough to decrease my tan line chances and let me enjoy my me time.

Well, of course that didn't work!

Now I think Bob has breached the boarder of my tranquility and is messing with me. I decide I will ignore him and stay the course.

Ha, in your face Bob! You can't distract me from my vintage cylinder of solitude!

Clearly my husband cannot be detoured because he has now started to up his game.

I reach down to my thigh prepared to slap the invaders hand but I am stopped abruptly when I do not feel anything of the husband variety.

What I do feel, is a creepy crawly bug about the size of a quarter making its way up my leg!

Oh my shit!

I fling the canopy of the tanning bed up like my life depended on it, because it does!!!

I sit up while screaming only to have the 40 pound cylinder of solitude canopy come crashing down on my head!

Now, I not only have a bug on my very naked flesh but I am pretty sure I have a cylinder of solitude concussion to go with it.

I decide to roll out of the bed onto the she shed floor to escape the bug that has yet to be identified.

This should be a moment my hero would come to my rescue! I mean, I did just scream for my life!

It appears, however, the beautiful sounds of Lanco can in fact drown out the screams of a naked 52 year old on all fours wearing neon pink tanning goggles (fun fact and you are welcome).

Once I have escaped the tanner and am able to stand, I inspect my warm naked flesh for the invader.

I am creepy crawly critter free, whew!

Oh shit, where did it go?

I grab my shirt and shoes and dress like a middle schooler in gym class.

When I feel the important parts are covered I open the tanner and find the invader.

A freaking red wasp!

These bastards are the sons of Satan! There was a red wasp moving freely on my naked flesh while I plotted evil things to get even with my husband!

I pulled a towel off the shelf and removed the little demon from my cylinder of solitude. I dropped the towel and stomp that spawn of Satan into a stain.

I think a moratorium is required from the she shed and the cylinder of solitude until all living things are permanently eradicated.

Me time- 0, Ozark demons- 1!

On to more productive ventures!

Bob and I decided to research our internet options. In this day of advanced technology no web should be buffering or pause for loading. Even this far off the grid we should be afforded the same benefits of all web users, right?

After spending the morning with the satellite internet provider to confirm the sad details of poor service we were forced to move on to the local phone company.

Now in this day of the cell phone most people have abandoned home services but it is apparently a requirement to get internet service that moves faster than a snail over a Velcro strip.

We have not had home phone service in several years so I didn't even have a phone to plug into the wall. Walmart it was, in search of the home phone to plug into the wall.

Since we have unlimited everything on our current cell provider the phone just needed to be basic. A simple phone with push buttons and no caller id screen will suffice.

If I could have scored an old school dial phone with a 25 foot cord I would have jumped on it (ahhhhh memories).

We arrive home and plug in the flash back to all things 90's and wait. The phone guys make the long trek down the driveway after locating our cattle gate and connect us to the rest of civilization in record time.

Bob and I couldn't wait to connect to the new buffering free life and surf like it's the perfect wave on the warm beaches of California.

We have been removed from such luxuries for almost 2 years but it feels like centuries.

Before I even realize it, it's time to pick up our grandsons from school!

One forgets how distracting the statuses of our Facebook, Instagram and Twitter feeds can become after 2 years of buffering.

I arrive at the school in time to load the 2 boys and make the trip back home. Declan will be over the moon excited that his iPad will fly through his YouTube searches (it's what kids love these days, kids watching kids play with toys).

When we enter the house I tell Ryland we have a home phone so he can call his friends when he wants after school. Ryland is pretty excited since he has had to borrow a cellphone to call his buddies. Ryland enters the den and reaches for the piece of history with the most perplexed look on his face.

I forget he is 9 but am quickly reminded when he looks up and says..... "how do you get on the Internet with this" ?

Whaaaat?

I tell him it's a phone, you make calls on it. He looks
the phone over again and says " how do you text?".
Oh lord have mercy!
We live in a world where kids will never know the
struggle of ducking the cord!
I again explain that you push the numbers and you
talk into the phone when the person answers, it's
called a phone call. Ryland puts the phone back in the
cradle with a sigh and advises us he is going to get on
his tablet and message Eli.
Well, we tried to broaden their horizons.

So now onto the television upgrades to go along with
our new warp speed web adventure.

A girl can dream, right?

I will start with "For once this did not happen to me!"

Bob has been working hard at switching from Dish to
just regular tv. I mean we really don't watch a lot of tv

so we decided with the legit internet we would research internet tv for the boys, woohoo.

We ordered a Fire Stick but also picked up a Roku to check it all out.

Oh my gracious can you get a lot of tv with that stuff!

Well, Bob also decided that if we put a small antenna outside we could get a lot of local HD channels (we live on a mountain for heavens sake).

I tell you all that to move on to this....

I took off to pick the boys up at school giving Bob a little alone time. In my absence, Bob installed an antenna off the deck to test what channels he could get.

Now with this experiment he had to run a cable from the antenna on the deck into the house.

Pretty simple really just open the patio doors and run it through the dining room right on into the living room tv.

Let the experiment begin....right?

Now, I keep a bird feeder on the deck for our feathered friends and always throw bread to the larger birds.

I figure if I keep the birds coming around they in turn will keep the snakes away (great plan I know).

Ok, so in my absence with patio doors open (weather is not bad so it's all working out) Bob is scanning channels when something catches his attention.

Again, it didn't happen on my watch (silently doing the happy dance during my briefing).

Apparently one of my little feathered buddies decided to enter through the open patio doors at mach speed and bounce like a superball off the living room window (about 40 feet give or take).

Bob now has to halt all channel research and retrieve said feathered missile before I get home with the boys (I do not want to explain that carnage to these little guys).

As Bob gets to the window to remove the lifeless bird it decides at this point to get up. It then takes the 3am bar walk with jello knees essentially shaking it off.

Bob gets a little closer to the ode to closing time just as he decides to bunny hop straight into our newly decorated 9 foot Christmas tree.

Bob now has to locate the semi conscious bird and attempt to evict the squatter before we have to explain "no, we can't keep it" to the boys.

Upon inspection of the tree Bob finds the bird hanging upside down in true bat form looking a little dazed.

So the Nut Hatch (finally id'd and confirmed harmless) gets spooked and takes flight into yet another window.

He does not get punch drunk off this second hit but it does slow him down.

Bob, with all his newly found zoo keeper skills, gets the little guy to actually exit the premises with nothing but a good story to share with his feathered friends.

By the time the boys and I get home Bob has recovered from his feathered frenzy and was calm as a cucumber as he shared the details with us. The boys find this story captivating and have a million questions but the first thing Declan does...

He opens the patio doors looking for the bird to come back.

Bob is quick to explain that the doors stay shut and Declan reluctantly complies. I love it when the insanity of our new surroundings touches someone else!

So now with the bird free television upgrades we are able to broaden the horizons of these little guys.

We are the proud owners of both a Roku and a Firestick after all.

These are truly amazing inventions to those of us who grew up watching 4 channels. We were blessed with a grainy pictures that required getting up to change channels but not disrupting the foil rabbit ears.

Fun fact on the new tv stick things, they have a feature called Alexa.

Now, I know nothing about this phantom voice that knows far too much information. I do, however, know her (of course it's female, sheesh) powers can provide endless entertainment to children of all ages (yes, Bob too).

It isn't until I am blissfully baking in my kitchen that I am enlightened of the technology marvels draw.

I start hearing a ping that sounds like an incoming text followed by an "ok" in the living room.

This has now captured my full attention (Bob showed the boys how to work the new devices).

I peer into the living room and see Declan playing with his farm play set while Ryland is doing homework. Very strange because I know I heard the tv talking. I walk over to the den to see Bob watching yet another automobile channel. Maybe Bob was searching something and my aging ears were playing tricks on me.

I head back to the kitchen just as another ping goes off.

I am not going crazy and I am not hearing things. That ping came from the living room!

I walk back over to the living room and quietly stand in the doorway. What I expect to see is Declan asking Alexa to find Open Season on anything.

What I do see is the blank screen on the tv but Ryland picking up the remote.

This is very intriguing as Ryland knows there are no electronics until homework is done. Typically we do this together but lately he has been more independent and showing me he can do more things on his own (sigh-he is maturing).

I wait like any good Nana and watch in shock as Ryland says "what is 64 divided by 9" into the remote!

Oh my shit!

Alexa is helping Ryland with his homework only the bitch is giving him the answers! I have been replaced by a far more lenient homework helper and my husband brought her in the house!

I step into the living room just as Ryland looks up at me and sets the remote aside.

Busted!

Ryland packs up his books and the rest of his supplies and carries them into the kitchen. We (Ryland and I) finish Ryland's homework without even bringing up that trader Alexa.

Let it be known from this day forward all homework will be done in the kitchen. The kitchen, where that genius in a stick can't tempt Ryland's developing mind with her evil ways.

Parenting and Grand-parenting is hard ya'll and with today's technology if we aren't careful we could send our future backwards.

With Christmas fast approaching we start with some traditions like baking and decorating etc..

In keeping with traditions, the boys and I decided to work on Christmas cards (mid December, I know-slacker). Now Declan is all about the stickers and Ryland decided at that point he would be more helpful watching YouTube tv (damn technology).

Declan and and I are making an unholy mess with stickers, one that I will spend hours cleaning up once they head back to their moms house.

Go me!

Declan decides he's had enough Nana time and says "I go see Papa and Uncle John at the shop".

Now these boys go to the shop to play all the time while Bob is out there working so I figured it was fine. I could finish up the cards and start cleaning up while Declan played in the shop.

As I am working Ryland says "do you know Declan is outside in your boots with no pants on?"

What?!

He had clothes on today!

It's Declan so it is rare he has on more than just underwear so I know I am right. As I look out the window I see Declan wearing my pink rain boots that are knee high on me but they are butt high on Declan. I do see that he does in fact have pants on and a jacket.

We have gotten a lot of rain lately so the driveway is loaded with big puddles.

Lots of big, muddy puddles.

Declan apparently felt my rain boots were actually scuba gear and was not only sitting in the largest muddiest puddle but he was doing it in my boots and..... Ryland's jacket!

Bob and I both witness the atrocity about the same time.

I see Bob come out of the shop to retrieve Declan from Lake Burdette and bring him to the house at the same time I am putting on my shoes.

When Bob and the boy get into the house we start stripping Declan to get him cleaned up. Mud dripping everywhere and my cute pink boots loaded with the same yuck water that is coating my grandson.

Once Declan was stripped and the washing machine started, it was bath time.

Declan is finicky when it comes to bath time. Always on his terms but today with mud dripping off his butt crack it was Nana terms.

I get the bath all ready and of course with the mud puddle training he just went through Declan jumps into the full tub shooting puddles of muddy bathwater all over my bathroom!

When I tell Declan he is going to help me clean up the mud, his response was simply "I am not muddy, Declan is all clean, Nana needs to clean". Hmmmm, I think there is still some work to do on these little guys.......pray for me.

There are days I reflect on my childhood that remind me of so much I see today. I recall being a little snarky at a young age much like my grandsons today. I remember mom sitting me down and giving me the look, most of you know all about THE LOOK. You know the one that makes you question everything you have ever said?

Well, I can tell you the look I got was followed by some bone chilling wisdom.

When your mother looks at you and says "one day, you will have a child and that child will be just like you. It is then that I will get my revenge"(shudder).

Now, if your mom never advised you of said wisdom I am sure she wanted to save you from years of worry. My mom chose to give this nugget as a warning and trust me I see it all clearly now. Part of me wondered which of the eight of my mothers children was her mothers warning. I am pretty sure it's my sister Vickie because there is no way it's me........is it?

I mean mom got paid to not skip school (I did quit kindergarten).

She got caught smoking in high school (I broke a window in the gym).

She took it upon herself to dye her jet black hair a platinum blonde much to my grandfathers horror (I did give myself a perm).

Oh shit!

It could be me and not Vickie.

After 52 years of living, I think I am the warning shot my grandma fired!

Dang!

Ok, so I shared this snippet of wisdom with my daughter at an early age.

I mean she was grounded for 2 years for gods sake! We took her bedroom door for weeks when she wouldn't stop slamming it.

She was my warning! Casie was my mothers warning and I even called my mother to apologize after that awakening.

All this seems relatively harmless until your grandson comes to you pleading to remove "the curse".

What?

Apparently one of the many things I taught my daughter was the "one day you will have a child and that child will be just like you. It is then that I will get my revenge" who chose to pass that onto her 9 year old son.

Ryland is trying at times but is typically a good kid. He was having a tough week and his mother felt it was time to pull out the big guns as his warning.

Ryland, however, felt this was a curse that I put on his mom that she then placed on him causing him to misbehave. So when he came to me pleading to remove the curse so he could stop getting in trouble I had no choice.

I sat Ryland down and explained that this was no curse and he really has to own his behavior but he can correct it and avoid discipline.

I was rewarded with "no, it's the curse you have to stop it!".

The things we do for our grandchildren........

I held Ryland's hand and looked into his sad eyes and simply said "One day you will have a child and that child will be perfect. You will love that child with your whole heart and they will make you proud."

That sounded good, right? I mean he should love that he isn't carrying the curse on to his kids.

Ryland looked up at me and replied with "how does that help me now? You didn't remove the curse!"

Think fast, this kid is smart.

I advised Ryland I wasn't done yet and continued with "you will be the example to your children and starting now you will be amazing."

I think that pacified him, unfortunately the impact to his behavior was not immediate. I can say with a clear conscience, my hands are clean.

My golden years in the Ozarks are proving to be a lot more work than I was banking on. Not only am I entering that phase in life that proves challenging but it would seem the weather here is as hormonal as I am. One winter day it's 65 degrees next day 32 and heavy winds (ok, in all fairness I do get the rapid temperature changes but under no circumstances do I have days with heavy wind- just so we are clear).

I am still not great with the huge wind gusts but we have a NOAA weather radio to alert us of really scary stuff. I gotta say that when that radio goes off in the dead of the night you better hope you have an empty bladder.

I tell you this so I can share the events of yesterday.

Bob and I found Declan's goldfish, that he has had for 2 years, floating belly up. I had to pick the boys up from school today because they were ours for the next 4 days. Now we were one perfect goldfish short of a normal weekend.

In my infinite wisdom I decided to run to Wal-Mart and replace belly up Dori before Declan discovers the travesty.

Once I get to the fish section I see these cute little orange and white fish as well as a Dori clone (it is seriously my devoted worship to all things Jason Momoa aka Aquaman that this is going so well). I ask the fish wrangler to add the 3 little fish to my Dori clone and I would explain to the boys that Dori needed friends so we brought the little guys home.

I cleaned the tank and loaded Destiny back in (plecostomus, they never die) before adding the 4 new fish (3 new and Dori clone). Feeling pretty good about this ruse I head out to pick up the boys.

Both boys get in the Jeep excited about school and staying at "NanaPapa's house" so the ride home went well.

Once inside and backpacks are emptied the boys go to check on Dori. Excited to see the little fish they ask if Dori had babies.

I quickly squash that notion as I am not explaining how that happens and tell them Papa and I brought home friends for Dori.

Declan is excited about the "cushe little babies" and wants to name them. I am thinking "how sweet is this little guy ?"

Declan points to the smallest fish and says "Aww that's Beau".

Ok, we now have Dori and Beau good start.

Then he points to the next new baby and says "that's Ryland" and the final fish is of course Declan. So I reiterate to Declan "so we have Beau, Ryland, Declan, Destiny and Dori?"

Declan looks at me with confusion on his face and says "that's not Dori that Damnitnoah".

Wait, what?

That fish is the perfect clone pulled from the alter of all things Momoa!

There is no way he can tell it isn't Dori!

I ask Declan again what that fish's name is.

Declan replies "Damn. It. Noah!" so that I understand him completely.

I immediately thought about the Jesuschristnancy from my childhood and understood where Damn It Noah came from (Nana fail).

I spent this morning explaining that Noah was a better name for Dori and pray he doesn't share his fish story with the first grade today.....in the event he did share, I am terribly sorry Mrs. Brewer, I tried.

Life is definitely interesting when you are surrounded by little people. I pray this gets easier as the years roll by. I can only imagine what their teenage years will bring to this crazy mix. I can assure you my own childhood did not prepare me for the children of today.

Growing up in a small town it was a right of passage when you turned 18 because you finally got to go to bingo.

I know what your thinking, "bingo is the Cabo for the blue hairs of the world, why on earth would a teenager go to bingo?"
I reiterate, small rural town and not a lot to do at night.

Back to my right of passage....

So on my 18th birthday my parents took me to play my first game of bingo. My dad was certainly enjoying this (I think it was mostly because I was the 6th child out of the 8 of us to turn 18, only 2 left until the party could really start). Bingo halls not only supplied all things gambling related but also peddled vast arrays of baked goods.

My dad raved on the homemade pies and in turn purchased a slice for me. Dad presented me with a lovely slice of strawberry pie to enjoy while I played my very first bingo card.

Now is a good time to point out that I have been allergic to berries my whole life. I found this out at the young age of 4 when I devoured my grandmothers strawberry patch and was rewarded with an entire body of hives. The doctors assured my mother this is something most children outgrow and just monitor me. I never wanted to go through that hell again so I avoided all berries from that moment on.

Mom assures me the small amount of berries in this slice of pie shouldn't hurt me since I have more than likely outgrown the allergy.

It wasn't long before the welts began and the itching started. Clearly I had not outgrown the allergy and my very first bingo experience was cut short.

I have explained all that to get to this....

My dad wanted to get out of the house (this is a positive step) so my sisters and I decided to join him at bingo.

Now I haven't been to bingo since the pie debacle so I thought this would be fun.

We haven't lived here all that long so I didn't know many people outside of family. This could be good for me too.

As I enter the bingo hall I feel very out of place but quickly locate my family. My sister Pam gets me set up with the cards I needed and I was ready to play. My sister Vickie pointed out people and how they know them. Vickie begins to explain things mom did when she would come to bingo and dad would add in details now and then. It was nice to be able to have this time together and hear about things I didn't know.

It's when Vickie points to a woman and says "that's the lady mom gave the Arkansas sex stones to" that absolutely has my full attention. I was completely shocked and waiting on details. I look to dad for more but he just shook his head and laughed.

I need more here!

You can't just drop a bomb like this and laugh, I was 9 hours away when this happened! What in the heck is an Arkansas sex stone and why am I just hearing of this?

I must have looked like a starving child because Vickie took pity on me and began the explanation.

Mom decided to take a baggie of stones to bingo and gift them to a woman. Mom loved pulling pranks and telling stories to anyone near her. When mom set the stones in front of the woman she was met with questions. The woman asked what they were and mom replied "these are Arkansas sex stones and I am giving them to you" the woman was confused and asked my mom "what are they and what do they do?" Mom replied they were "Arkansas sex stones, you do what you want with them".

The woman, very confused, asked again "what are they?"

Mom replied "They are fucking rocks!"

Oh my gracious!

I looked at my dad and asked "what did you say?" to which he replied "jesuschristnancy".

Thank god bingo started, I am not sure where these stories took a turn but I was pretty sure that was a good stopping point.

I realized it had been quite some time since I had played bingo but it took no time to realize I was out of my element.

I am convinced that bingo caller was an Aldi cashier in her day job because she was shooting out those numbers like she was on Redbull and Pixie Stix.

I was only playing a couple cards but dear lord I was legit afraid to blink and God forbid I needed a drink or worse yet pee.

Needless to say bingo proved very informative but in no way lucrative. I am pretty sure I can go another 34 years before I put myself through that hell again.

Time to find a hobby.

The weather here was starting to feel more like a mild winter with cooler temps in the evenings. Bob and I decided we would begin using the fireplace in the den at night to provide additional warmth and ambiance.

On this particular evening the house was quiet and the boys were with their mom so fire, movie and a little wine were on the agenda.

I had started to drink lots of water during the day as it seemed to help keep hot flashes at bay (that could be yet a another song, man am I gifted).

Anyway, so Bob and I are cuddled up in the den with a fire glowing, Netflix playing and wine flowing. There is no better way to let the day melt away than the vibe we have right here, right now.

Bob and I have been together nearly 37 years and been married for 34 of them. We raised 3 children and both worked full time jobs outside the home. This right here is what we worked so hard for.

A few hours and several glasses of wine later it was time to call it a night. I was ready to curl up in that big warm bed and sleep in. I didn't have to get the boys off to school in the morning and we had no plans. Maybe this retirement life was really going to be ok. Bob and I spent every day and night together. We ate every meal together, worked outside together and even relaxed together.

Sure there were things we needed to work on.

For instance, Bob really needed to stop balling his socks up in pairs before throwing them in the laundry. That drives me insane.

Anyway, back to our relaxing evening.

I was exhausted and ready to sleep longer than Rip Van Winkle and deeper than Sleeping Beauty. I needed this and there was nothing that required my attention to stop my plan.

Ok, unless you consider the several glasses of wine, the fact I gave birth 3 times and my walnut size bladder. Yup, I have come to the point in my life where I need to pee a couple of times during the night. Like clockwork I get up from a sound sleep and make my way to the bathroom. My eyes still closed and feet sluggish but I have made this trip enough to know my way. I reach the bathroom grab the ring and put it down (another thing Bob has to work on). I am surrounded by males here and every bathroom in this house is left with the ring up! I have dealt with this for so long I don't even complain any more.

As I was saying, I drop the ring and plop down to rid myself of my inner most thoughts when I am instantly brought to life!

Not like George Clooney in ER working a defibrillator to bring me back to life (sigh).

Nope, more like an ice bucket challenge that went seriously wrong. The frozen chill that raced from my bits to my heart had me breathing like I just completed the Chicago marathon!

Holy shit!

I was the last person in this bathroom and the ring was securely in place before I put the "ring" down!

I apparently put the lid down in my groggy state and that folks is the worlds worst alarm!

I no longer had to pee and I am pretty sure the very tender part of my feminine bits retreated to my lungs.

The struggle with aging isn't just visible even if 50 is the new 30.

It is, isn't it?

Don't tell me, I prefer to be left with my delusions.

So now that I am awake and no chance of going back to bed I decide to start my day.

I take a nice hot shower (hoping my nether region can recover from the polar vortex) and get ready to meet the day.

I start flossing my teeth and as I am yanking the floss I hear a small ping. What the hell was I eating in my sleep that would sound like a bb? As I am running my tongue along my teeth I feel a small hole. Oh my god, I think I broke a tooth!

Well, upon inspection, I lost a micro filling while flossing. This filling was so small and had to have been old because I was unaware I had it.

Oh my god!

I have to call a dentist, a new Ozark dentist!

I have never had any issue going to the dentist and I love taking care of my teeth. I am keeping these bad boys as long as possible. There is no way I am gumming my meals or shooting dentures out with a sneeze.

Ozark dentist it is......

So I am lucky enough to get into a dentist who is right in town and on my insurance.

Things are looking up!

As I am waiting to be called back I begin to read the AARP paper we got in the mail. I am not old so stop thinking those horrible thoughts, 50 is in fact the new 30!

So back to my reading literature.....

I find a lengthy article on "ways to add healthy years to your life".

Well now that I am 30 I guess I should read it.

It lists several things to change, exercise, diet, blood pressure, blah, blah, blah etc.. Normal stuff we all know but typically never heed.

It wasn't until I got deeper in to the read that shit got real.

Waist to height ratio (oh no), your waist circumference should be less than half your height to ward off dangerous belly fat.....

Damn, that sucks.

Pretty sure it will be easier to grow that foot and a half than shrink my waist.

Respect the Z's, get a regular sleep pattern and keep it.

Boom, nailed that one!

This chick loves her night time slumber.

See a dentist at least twice a year.

Ummmm, I am sitting here as I read this, nailed it!

The Get Up Test, what the hell is a get up test?

Apparently you need to sit on the floor and without hands, help or furniture you need to get to the standing position.

You have got to be kidding me?

I am pretty sure I couldn't do that in high school!

Thank god the dentist called me back because reading about aging was sucking the life out of me.

I follow the tech back to the chair where she asks why I was there. I simply explained I was flossing and lost a small filling. She was very nice and took a look then walked to the hall.

Ok, I guess I wait for the dentist to come in, no biggie. I sure as hell am not reading any more about aging while I wait.

As I am inspecting the room for dust bunnies I hear the tech say, "we have a flosser"!

What?!

The dentist comes in and sits in front of me ready to go.

Well that was fast, we are moving right along.

The tech then says "we have a flosser here".

Is that shit code or are they legit stunned that I freaking floss?

I mean if that's code for anything I should know someone better share that information asap!

The dentist looks at the tooth in question and without hesitation starts to work.

Dang, these guys work fast!

As this southern stranger is 10 fingers in, he starts making small talk.

Questions?

I have a mouth full of cotton and southern man hands, there was no way I am responding.

About 3 questions in the dentist removes his hands and its my turn to speak.

I am really good at many things but conversation with a mouth full of fingers?

Not so much.

Long story short......

Tooth fixed in under 20 minutes and I had the whole day free, woohoo!

Well that was short lived elation.

Since the weather was so accommodating Bob and I decided we would do a little tree removal.

By little tree removal I mean 5 large trees that housed swarms of red wasps (aka spawns of Satan).

These select trees were really tall and too close to the house so they had to go.

After seeing what can happen to a house when a large tree does its best Mary Lou Retton floor routine, I was on board.

Bob has a chainsaw in tow and I have the golf cart full of supplies at the ready. We start with a smaller tree, Bob cuts a wedge on one side and cuts through on the other. The tree falls perfectly and we move on to tree number 2. Same process, same results. I am thinking this is going to be a breeze. Bob and I will be done in no time, this is gravy.

Yeah, I spoke way too soon.

As we are notching tree number 3, the tree starts to crack.

Oh my shit!

The tree starts to fall right where I am standing. Bob yells at me to move but I am freaking out! I am having tornado flashbacks and losing my shit!

Bob does his best to push the tree to the side as it falls to save me (my hero- most days). When the tree lands Bob looks at me and says"why didn't you move?"

Umm, that is a really good question and one I am sure I will answer when my hearts starts beating again!

After a little break in action I am back among the living.

Bob will always be my hero and today he stepped up his game.

Well, until enough time has passed and he feels its safe enough to say (with the most sympathetic look he can muster) "you are a magnet for natural disasters".

Wait, what!?

What part of that situation was natural?

I mean sure it had disaster written all over it.

Yes, shit seems to always find me I will give you that.

Under no circumstances will this go down as a natural disaster, no way!

My husband can be my biggest hero or my greatest revenge victim. Not sure which he is hoping to achieve today but I am pretty sure either way it is going to get interesting.

On to tree number 4, stay with me, we have 5 trees total.

So now we have tree number 4 cut with the wedge towards the hollar. Bob comes around to the side facing the house to put in the final cut.

Let me just say, we have watched all those logging shows on discovery channel, researched online and have had 66% success so far. We are in fact skilled professionals in the fine art of tree eradication (or so we thought).

When Bob makes the final cut the tree decides to go rogue and twists toward the house!

Oh my god!

This is a tall tree, if it doesn't turn it is taking out my deck!

As the tree falls in slow motion Bob and I just stare in disbelief, there is nothing we can do.

The tree makes contact with the roof over the deck with a loud thud!

I have my eyes closed so I have no idea how bad it is.

I hear Bob say a few curse words and I open my eyes.

The tree bounced off the roof but landed on the ground.

I look at Bob ready to defend myself from the whole magnet/disaster thing when he simply says "I think we are done for today, I better check the roof."

Only 3 shingles were harmed in this process!

Time to buy lottery tickets, for once things were actually going in our favor! I am certain it won't last long but I will take it.

Move forward a few days and it was time to trim the branches off the fallen trees and cut up some firewood.

As we are cutting off the smaller limbs and stacking them in piles for chipping Bob decides we need to move the bigger limbs down to the fence line. By fence line I mean hollar, by we I mean me. As I am walking down this hillside in shorts and chore boots (trend setter that I am) I start pulling the heavier limbs behind me. Once I hit the fence line I start shoving the limbs in the tangled hell of rose thorns and poison everything. I make a few trips and can really feel the burn in my calves and thighs. Bob has since hopped on the tractor to assist me. On my eighth trip into the Devils lair of all things sharp I get tangled up in some vines. As I pull myself out of the vines straight off the Jumanji set I get caught by a cluster of wild rose bushes.

You have got to be kidding me!

I start pulling thorns out of my legs when I feel something on my arm.

Mother Mary and Joseph!

A big black hairy spider has decided to make my arm his home! He is staring at me and giving me the "lets throw down" look! I can feel him preparing his fangs (that are as big as elephant tusks) for the feast of my forearm! I lock eyes with this demon and contemplate using the limb in my hand as a weapon! The only thing saving this spider from certain death is my fear of killing myself with said limb.

That's it!

I have been impaled by thorns, accosted by vines and been far too close to God only knows what type of venomous arachnid I just threw into the hollar!

I am done!

Well, I would be done if all my energy wasn't just spent flailing like Phoebe on Friends running through Central Park (seriously, google it). I am stuck at the bottom of a very steep hillside and may have to send out smoke signals for help.

God I hope the burn ban was lifted!

Just when I am about to have a full on meltdown Bob comes down the hillside on a tractor! It's not a Whitehorse but Bob is in fact my knight in Carhart so I take it. He pulls the tractor next to me and I latch on like it's the last game system on Black Friday! Bob pulls me up the hillside to safety and I take that as my much deserved break.

In my excited break bliss I notice that the boys are mysteriously quiet and nowhere to be seen.

The boys were helping move the split wood to the front porch. They were loading the wagon and pulling it around front and stacking it. They had pulled two loads but I had not seen them come back. I decide my break was over before it began and hopped on the golf cart to locate our helpers.

As I make my way around the house to the front I see a full wagon parked but definitely no activity working to unload it. As I get closer to the front of the house I see that the boys have decided they needed a trampoline break. They were working hard and not trying to kill one another so if they wanted a break I was ok with it. What I didn't expect to see was all their clothes laying on the ground next to their boots. The boys were jumping on the trampoline in the middle of February in their underwear!

There are days when adulting is just too hard and today was no exception. It took hostage negotiating skills to get them to get their clothes on but I lacked the skill to get them back to work.

I will take this as a win and never mention it again.

I thought raising kids was hard in the 90's but the kids of today have so many outside influences that make parenting a lot harder than we had it.

As young parents Bob and I would discuss what we wanted for our children. What we hoped they could achieve but first and foremost we wanted them happy. No matter where life's path took them we wanted each of our children to find true happiness.

We hoped to teach them compassion, forgiveness and love. There were times we felt we were failing them when life got hard. We always hoped it would teach them so much more. We wanted our sons to be kind, loving husbands and fathers (or pro athletes). We hoped our daughter would be a strong compassionate wife and mother. Above all else we wanted all our children to be honest, truly good humans.

My parents were the very same. They instilled in us all the essential values to be good people. Mom never lost her sense of humor no matter what life threw at her. Mom battled various forms of cancer for years but never let it break her spirit. She had cancer removed from her nose that required skin grafts. Mom refused to let the skin come from her butt (because apparently thats a thing). They used some from her forehead instead but she said she had "plenty of wrinkles they could pull from and it was better than having a butt face". Believe me, I am shaking my head and smiling remembering this conversation. A few years later mom had to undergo an emergency mastectomy. The mastectomy left a lot of excess skin where her breast once was. Moms response for her follow up appointment with the doctor was to fold the skin over into a purse and tape it closed. The doctor was more than shocked at this little stunt and made her remove it. Mom said he had no sense of humor and dad, well he just shook his head.

I hope that no matter what life throws at me, my husband, children or my grandchildren we have the same view on life my mom did.

There are so many times in life we face challenges that could break us but it's how we react to them that defines us.

I hope, with all the crazy this new life has thrown at us, we can at least show the boys this very thing. Challenges should never break us, they should make us stronger.

Time to test that theory.....

My plan today was to relax and enjoy my morning.... (heavy sigh)

You see the gentleman that owns the cattle mafia was delivering bales of something green to feed the herd early today.

He owns them and even he knows to stay on their good side.

That's an eye opening revelation!

So anyway, while one of the employees was being the Bovine Dominos delivery driver, a rogue bale of dinner ended up in my driveway.

Now this driveway is one (sketchy as hell) lane, so bale dodging won't send Dog the Bounty Hunter to bring you in safely. Nope, it would take you on the sledding through a plinko game bouncing off trees until you reach the bottom, wherever the hell that is. So clearly the bale (of item to be named later) needed relocation so I could navigate yet another trip to town. I put the jeep in park and attempted to lift the bale and move it to the side but realized quickly these things are as compliant as putting socks on a two year old. This thing was flopping around like an rainbow trout on crack. There was no moving this to the safe side of the road. I decided to just flip it towards the hollar from hell and hope for the best.

I did not plan on my Ozark Hulk abilities to kick in and have this thing flip 6 feet down the hillside-dang!

Now I look around and see 3 older calves up on the hill behind me. I felt like the mom eating the last Oreo with a house full of toddlers. Guilt of tossing their treat was eating at me. I felt the bovine mafia watching and judging my every move. This bale was visible but in no way reachable to the hungry herd. It was like I hung a sign "see the candy, can't have it"!

I had to brave this sketchy hillside to retrieve the rogue bale and get it close enough so the cows could eat it!

I never signed up for this, how did I get to this point in my life?

I look in the passenger seat of the jeep at Ryland who is enjoying my torture and wave him over. I am not going down alone, no way!

Ryland volunteers to grab the string on the bale and I will pull both Ryland and the bale to safety. This plan was perfect unless you consider..me, the hollar and Ryland.

Ryland grabs the string on the bale and I begin to pull him and the bale up to the road. Ryland is holding on like his life depends on it, because, well it does. The string releases the bale and sends us backwards and we are left with nothing but dirt on our butts!

This bale has 2 strings left we will make this work. We line up and try again to get this bovine buffet out of the hollar!

Ryland indicates he is ready so I pull with everything I have, Ryland and the bale come to the edge of the driveway. Ryland then releases the string and the bale explodes all over the driveway, great!

Now there is no way to relocate this feast but it is in fact accessible to "the family". I look at the Bovine audience and am met with a head nod. I kid you not these guys are seriously not to be messed with.

I tell you all that to get to my point. With all our great intentions and good deeds I was rewarded with .... a freaking tick bite behind my ear!

Now an Ozark tick bite can be compared to taking a nail gun and shooting not one, not two but three nails through your hand then rinsing the wound thoroughly with lemon juice. These little creatures spend their off time in a hot tub of venom right next to the red wasps! I have come to the conclusion that any critter in the Ozarks that can bite, sting or lick you has the power to take out grown men by the dozens. They are not to be messed with and they can ruin your week!

Message received bovine mafia, message received!

I will never mess with your territory or items in it.

I will simply take my chances and go around it....

Pause for shopping challenges.....

If you are one of these shoppers, no offense intended but you have in fact been warned.

When a store is busy it can become difficult to navigate aisles.

I mean, I too have had my..."look, a squirrel" moment.

Checkout lanes that are packed so long they cause traffic issues in the aisles also fire my rage.

I personally choose not to utilize those self checkouts as I prefer to support workers who are supporting themselves or families (whew, that was long winded).

Back to my point....

If by chance, you run into your 2nd grade teachers neighbors cousin and decide to talk, that's fine I am a patient woman. I am not competing in supermarket sweeps, I am beyond cool with it.

If you decide to walk away from your cart while blocking an aisle during said busy time to go 2 aisles over.......it is game on.

If you should find any additional shopping treasures while checking out....you are in fact one of those people.

KY, Vagisil, condoms and Depends will appear in your cart and may even make it home with you. It has been just that kind of day!

I feel this is far more therapeutic than coming at you like a spider monkey with a serious Pez addiction. You have been warned and should actively work on your shopping cart etiquette.

See, challenges can make you stronger and can be educational too.

A much needed quiet night was in the works.

A fire and a little movie time in the den. This was a Wednesday that was feeling like a Friday (retirement has its advantages).

As Bob and I are relaxing we hear that the wind has picked up outside. Seems to be a frequent occurrence in our new home. As we are intently watching Netflix we hear a thud coming from what we thought was upstairs. Now the boys are not here so there is no one upstairs, Bob asks if I was going to investigate.

Nope, not me, no way (magnet/disaster?).

I explain, I think a screen blew off the window in the spare bedroom and he should head upstairs so he can fix it. About the same time we hear a loud thud but this one is coming from the front porch. Now if a screen blew off upstairs it would make sense the wind would bring it down to land on the porch. Nancy Drew has nothing on me, I am a true detective (patting myself on the back).

Bob asks me to look outside and see if anything is on the porch (very dark and the lights weren't on). As Bob makes his way to the door, I stand to look out the den window. As I get close to the window, a very large black beast runs by the window heading toward the front door!

Dear god there is a wild beast on my porch!

The bear is back and he is hungry!

I grab my chest because I am certain I am having a heart attack and Bob is going to open the door!

I scream something to the affect of "oh god, black fur!"

Bob stops just shy of the door as lightening starts outside. This has the makings of every b grade horror flick ever made! I am going to be eaten in my new paradise!

I walk to the window hoping and not hoping (inner battle to save my sanity) to catch a glimpse of my killer.

When I get to the pearly gates I can provide as much detail as possible. If I survive the attack I can let the police know every detail of the assault.

As I look out the window Bob turns on the porch lights.

Just as I lean into the window to look out, a loud thud thunders outside and the freaking beast lunges at the window!

This is it, this is how I go out!

I scream with everything I have and Bob (my hero-most days) comes to look at the monstrous beast. As we are side by side looking into the black night, the giant beast lunges forward again and puts his front paws on the window right in front of me!

I. AM. DEAD!

Everything becomes a blur and I am pretty sure I just peed!

As I regain my senses Bob assures me I am in fact fine.

Bob identified my would be attacker and was headed outside to run it off the porch.

Did you know that a coon hound resembles a bear in the dark of night?

Well, I am here to tell you that both have the ability to make me lose my shit!

Apparently this mischievous giant was lost, hungry and very scared. Bob sat outside with him petting his head and calming him down while I cleared all leftovers from the fridge to feed him. He was thin and clearly looking for a meal. I was so relieved that the meal wasn't me, I grabbed everything I could carry to feed him.

Once this invader was fed and calmed down Bob placed a blanket on the porch for him to sleep on. He was fed, safe and warm for the night and we would find his family in the morning.

Instead of a restful sleep for being dog savers we were rewarded with the weather radio wake up calls every 2 hours. The radio was going off alerting us to tornados and severe weather in our area, gahhhh!

By 6am Bob was waking me up with "the sky is red we better get downstairs". I was out of bed and dressed in minutes (I am so over this whole tornado stuff).

Once we made it downstairs we found the fury invader curled up on the porch right where we left him. Bob went to the porch to check out our visitor and the sky. I went to the kitchen, if I was headed off to Oz, I was going with coffee. I started to cook some sausages for our guest. This guy needed to eat and I needed to stay busy. Once Rosco (Bob named him) was fed Bob decided to bring him into the house where it was safer. Bob played with the dog while I blew up Facebook looking for his family. Luckily his family was located after a few hours and they would be picking him up in the evening. The poor boy was lost for a few days after a hunting trip but was headed home to his family. These are the happy endings all fur parents hope for.

I for one, am certain, I won't survive another invader!

Time to pray for normal, whatever that may be these days.

Our typical daily routine keeps me sane. Picking up our grandsons from school and enjoying a little bit of kid time is great therapy. Declan usually takes videos of the animals we see and Ryland usually challenges me to a rap battle. Ryland finds great joy in trying to "burn" me and he is getting better at it.

Normally I would start with something simple like..........

I know this boy, who thinks he's cool.

Trying real hard not to be a fool.

Throws down rap to be all bad.

But his Nana just makes him look sad.

It generally ends up with him laughing about getting "torched", whatever that is.

Today was different.

Ryland didn't want to battle, he wanted to talk about getting dumped. His little girlfriend felt he wasn't serious enough and broke his little heart. I need to remind him all the time that he is 9. Not sure what serious is at 9 but I like the kid he is.

I asked him how he felt about it and if he was ok.

Ryland said he likes to be funny some times and he isn't ready for "serious" (he literally did air quotes).

I thought I would be the good Nana and explain that he is 9 and there will be plenty of girls in his life who will like him for who he is, he shouldn't be different for anyone. Ryland looked at me with understanding on his face and said " I know, I have friends who are girls and they aren't all full of drama. I mean they like me but I just like them as friends." This is good, he sees his worth and knows who he is, proud moment. He then asks if he can tell me something.

Oh no, am I ready for this?

He is serious and I do not know where this is going. I respond with "buddy you can always tell me anything, we talk all the time and I am here for you no matter what" (silently praying this is not something huge).

Ryland says "there are girls at school who like me like a girlfriend but I don't want to be mean". "I mean, I like them but like a friend not like a girlfriend".

At 9?

When did this confusing stuff start?

I mean there are adults who don't get it and here I am discussing this with a 9 year old. I explain to Ryland that it's ok to have friend feelings for girls and not think every girl he likes is a potential girlfriend. I explained that "the girl you choose to be your girlfriend should also be a friend, Papa is my best friend". Ryland nodded his head in understanding and said " I don't want to be mean, I think friends is ok because if I break their heart then they won't be friends, isn't that right?"

Wow!

Reminding myself he is 9 is tough when he makes a statement like that. I guess raising good humans isn't that hard after all. If he gets this at 9 and doesn't forget it when puberty strikes then we actually have fewer battles ahead.

The next day when it was time for pick up, Ryland was back to the happy little man I love.

His little heartbreaker changed her mind and she was ready for commitment again.

I asked him if he was happy about her change of heart. Ryland responded with "yeah, but I think if she does it again I am done. I don't need that kind of drama in my life right now".

Adults could learn a lot from this kid..........

Time for a grocery run........

To most that isn't big deal, to us it means loading up the cooler that is large enough to house an adult body and grab every eco-friendly bag I own.

Make the drive down the mountain and grab dad so we could make the 2.5 hour drive to Harrison.

Harrison has an Aldi and they are NOT a dry county (double win).

We load up on groceries and lunch before the long drive home. We make it a point to visit a new restaurant each time so we can broaden our horizons. Dad really enjoys the hunt for a new place to have lunch.

We take this long trip once a month and it is well worth it.

I have said all that to bring you to the events of today.

As we are making our way down the mile long driveway, we see the cows are once again in the field. Cute little calves are grazing and playing on the right side of the drive. I look to the left and see about a dozen wild turkeys (not the liquid courage kind) some of which appear to be huge. Not that I have a vast knowledge of turkeys that aren't on my table at Thanksgiving but these were in fact big.

As we progress further down the driveway the turkeys begin to scatter. While watching them disperse I see that the "huge" turkeys were not huge at all. The turkeys were using my driveway as Miss Nana's house of ill repute! The turkey flock began to disengage from their fornication folly and became 20 scrambling turkeys!

I looked at Bob in horror!

There are some things in life you never want to see because you can't unsee them, this is one of those things!

I am 52 and had no idea these gobble neck creatures were into public displays of affection!

Shouldn't they commit these acts in the shrubbery or better yet in the hollar from hell?

I had no idea it was done in the manner I just witnessed!

I certainly had no idea the "after"did not include cuddling!

Bob assures me that most animals in the wild do in fact procreate in this manner and it is in fact natures normal.

Ummmm........ I can assure you that what I just witnessed was in no way normal!

I have witnessed a bull take his procreating aggression out on a cow in my driveway (I lost all respect for the male bovine that day-*shudder*) and now turkeys!

I do not want to see this circle of life shit!

Let me just tell you that the untimely, abrupt dismount of turkey love will be burned in my memory for life.

I need to wear blinders in my own driveway!

Move to the Ozarks they said........

You will love being surrounded by nature they said.............

Ahhh....... yes, nature!

The 75 degree days were coming often so outdoor activities were a must.

The boys were on the trampoline enjoying the sun and fun that spring brings. They love being outside playing in the yard. I love watching them but today I had a few things that required my attention in the house. As I am cleaning up the kitchen and loading the dishwasher I hear a scream from the trampoline. Now most the noise these boys make while outside certainly resemble screams but this was different. I run to the door as Ryland is coming inside. Ryland is adamant that "a hawk just dive bombed" them. We see all kinds of birds daily and hawks are among those.

Declan was still outside on the trampoline enjoying himself so I decided to go out and check on the situation. I look around the trampoline but don't see anything concerning so I head back toward the house. My plan was to tell Ryland that he was seeing things but was stopped short when a woodpecker dropped from the sky right in front of me! The bird was lifeless and had a serious head wound.

I look up and see the Hannibal Lecter of the flying feathered world circling overhead! The large hawk was not even remotely concerned about my presence. I think he was actually giving me the side eye!

I had an eerie feeling this was beginning to take on a Godfatheresk horses head warning. I feed these birds, all of them, daily!

I am worried about my newfound feathered friends expectations and my apparent lack of loyalty that would provoke such a warning.

Apparently the hawk did in fact dive bomb my grandsons on his way to send this very real message! If he was closer I am certain I would have kissed his ring! For now, I have to retrieve the bloody carcass and get it to his final resting place before full panic sets in. I was not prepared for the amount of blood this guy was losing or the prying little eyes behind me.

I am learning far more about nature then I care to in this stage of my life.

Time to come inside and re-evaluate my devotion to these flying mobsters before something else decides to drop from the sky.

The weekend concluded without further incidents, that's a win.

The boys were headed back to their moms house for a couple days so we needed to get some work done. We had wiring in the barn to finish up but had to run to town first to grab a couple things.

While heading home Bob and I were in deep discussion about the warmer weather and getting the pool set up for the boys. Having a pool in the summer here is a must as long as I DO NOT fall asleep in it.

The conversation then changed to Aquaman since all things aquatic will forever be Jason Momoa related (see Bob gets me, he really does).

It's a 20 minute drive so we have plenty of time to bond.

At some point Bob broke into my Aquaman daze and shifted the conversation to "sometimes the beautiful ones are crazy", huh? Oh right, we are taking about people in general, this makes sense. Then he follows that up with "some people prefer the crazy because of the beautiful".

I thought about this for a minute, it was a pretty good point. We know a few people who could validate this.

I then replied with "some people love crazy and don't care what people look like". It's true some people are drawn to crazy like moth to a flame.

This is how we bond, over random nothing conversations (insert contented sigh here).

Bob agreed with me and then he turned to look at me.

It was this very moment I will remember for the rest of my life, the moment IT dawned on me.

You know the aha moment you get, like when algebra finally makes sense?

Yeah, I was having one of those moments and all thoughts of Aquaman left me like bad Chinese food!

For as far back as I can remember my husband has greeted me the in morning with "morning beautiful"....... Every morning!

Oh my god!

My husband of 34 years, my best friend, my partner in life, father of my children is essentially saying "yeah, you're crazy but the suns up!"

I think now is a good time to remind this man sitting next to me, the man of my dreams whom I love completely that I do in fact cook for him and he is treading on thin ice!!

Just another instance where I would plot my revenge.....husbands can be a handful, most days but today I let him slide.

I however, can't seem to ever catch a break.

No matter how well I shop I always need to make a quick run to town for something. Today I had to make a short trip to the local store for lettuce. If I went alone I could get in and out with just lettuce. Bob could entertain the boys for the 45 minutes it would take. That isn't hard, we have a plethora of kid stuff and every movie known to man.

As I am gathering my shoes and purse to make my escape Ryland stops me, of course. Ryland says he needs to go to the store too but assures me he won't beg for anything. I know this kid better than I know myself, he's going to ask (sigh). I tell Ryland to get his shoes on and we will go about the time Declan appears.

Now Declan wants to go but Declan is sporting tighty whiteys only! I guess I need to dress the boy in order to make my quick run to town with two boys in tow. I am shooting Bob the stink eye as I gather the boys and he just smirks in return. Yes, I am plotting my revenge and yes it will be memorable.

I should have known this was going to go sideways before I left home but I live with many delusions these days.

As we make the trip towards town Ryland is begging to "push the cart when we get to the store" so I agree (what harm can he do, right?). I park the jeep and get the boys out to run into the store for the lettuce. Once we enter this store Ryland immediately grabs the racecar cart that is as long as a minivan. Now both boys are too big for this cart but Ryland is adamant that he can push it. I just need to get lettuce so its no big deal if he wants to push that soccer mom cart around the store. We are just going to be here a couple minutes tops.

Declan takes this brief distraction to fold himself into the car at the front of this shoppers nightmare.

Ok, I just need lettuce so we head to the back of the store. On the way Ryland finds bakery donuts he can't live without and bacon (uggggg).

My short trip is now becoming an adventure (yup, I knew this was going to happen).

As we are turning toward the lettuce Ryland doesn't take into consideration that Declan is in the cart and does a Fast and Furious worthy drift slide into a display of Yummy Cakes!

Oh my god!

I quickly move to the front of the cart so I can stand the Leaning Tower of Pisa and stock the cakes back into their rightful place. Ryland gets redfaced but shrugs it off, apologizes and continues pushing Declan and the cart to the lettuce.

I grab the lettuce and try to rush these boys to a register to get out of here. As we are getting into the checkout line Ryland uses his new found driving skills to take out a giant meat sale sign at the front of the store.

There is no hiding this fail, I smile at the now staring crowd of customers and fix the sign ready to get out of here.

I check out and ask Ryland to put the cart away but my instruction should have been clearer. Ryland pushed the cart back just fine but he failed to let his brother get out of the car first!

I grab my change and the bag of groceries and run to the cart area to retrieve Declan. I have just aged 10 years in the 20 minutes I was in this store no doubt.

I get to the carts and pull the cart back out so Declan can escape and we can get home.

Problem is Declan can't get out of the cart! He was too big to get in but did it anyway and now he is stuck in this orange race car cart from hell!

I drop my purse and the groceries while trying to reach in to pull Declan out of the cart but I can't get him to budge!

God Help Me!

I am going to have to call the volunteer fire department to bring the jaws of life to get my grandson released from this plastic prison! All this hell because I wanted lettuce!

I am beginning to panic, I cannot get this child out and Ryland has joined in trying to pull his feet from the opposite side! Ryland and I are trying for about 10 minutes to free Declan when an older gentleman comes up and holds onto the cart. Then a 2nd gentleman comes over and pulls Declan's feet out the window of the car.

Now Declan is essentially planking half in, half out of the plastic prison and trying feverishly to belly crawl out (definitely not in Dukes of Hazard mode, more like fish on dry land) but it's working.

After a good 2 minutes of flailing Declan is free and laying belly up on the floor. I am pretty sure the hot flash I feel brewing is definitely going to big but I have to get out of here.

I thank the men and reach down to help Declan up when he looks at me and says "I'm not too big!".

I think the crowd we amassed would disagree but I let it go.

The lesson here is...avoid lettuce at all costs, nothing good can come from it ....EVER!!!

All I ask is for a couple days of disaster free fun and relaxation.

Summer is just around the corner.................

Today was a beautiful day and we decided to let boys ride the quad around the yard. Ryland has really become a cautious driver but as always we are right by them. I follow around on the golf cart and watch closely. Declan must have decided at one point Ryland was just too boring because he chose to join me in the golf cart.

The golf cart actually belongs to my brother John but when he dropped it off I noticed the seats were in need of repair. I decided to add my very own personal touches to it. I figure it may delay his retrieval of said golf cart if I recovered the seats in a wonderful electric pink upholstery (pretty sure he doesn't want to be seen sporting pink anything).

Now that I have Declan with me in the golf cart he is begging to drive. I have had zero luck surviving Declan's need for speed but of course I can't say no. I move over and let Declan have the wheel much to his delight and yes, I should have taken that as a warning.

Now this is in fact a golf cart so the gas pedal is a little tough to push, Declan is 7 and I am thinking this will be a breeze. What I failed to do was slide my foot under the gas pedal to limit the speed that Declan was allowed to reach. This would not have been all that serious had my husband not opened the gate to the mile long steep and bumpy driveway! When Declan saw the gate open it was as if the spirit of every dare devil that ever lived took control of this child. He passed through the gate and it was then that this 7 year old put full pressure on the gas pedal essentially flooring it! Declan hit the steep, curvy very bumpy part of the driveway and looked possessed. He was nearly standing on the pedal and steering like an Indy driver. Problem? The left side of the driveway borders the very scary side of the mountain dropping into a hollar. We hit a large bump and I reached for the wheel just as Declan jerked a hard right turn on the wheel! Couple of things I learned in that 30 seconds as my life passed before my eyes.

Never under any circumstances let Declan drive anything with me as the passenger no matter how cute he is.

Never make the above mistake with a full bladder!

I would love to say "just kidding" on that last point, however, my laundry would prove me a liar. Both Declan and I survived the driveway and made it back into the yard unscathed. Bob may not be that fortunate once I am able to speak again!

That is definitely a lesson learned folks, definitely a lesson learned!

I would like to think that with mother nature yanking my youth out of me like baby teeth to an apple she would in turn grant me some other superpower. Is it too much to ask for to at least have the power to foresee the crazy before it happens? I have no doubt that even then it will find me but at least I would be more prepared when I lose my shit!

So it appears with age not only do you show signs of aging but your body begins to age in silence. You start to brace yourself for a sneeze and hope you don't feel a pop or crack in your spinal column unlike your childhood where you let that sucker blast free spraying the world. Yup, life takes a drastic turn before you even realize your rapid decline with every birthday.

This brings me to the events of Saturday...sigh.

I climbed a ladder to put lightbulbs in my she-shed, lights my husband installed. He is going all out making this a cute little escape room homey and inviting. So I put in the bulbs and climbed down the ladder and felt a sharp pain in my hip and it shot down my leg light a knife wound! Seriously, I have jumped from a loft in a barn, climbed, jumped and fell out of trees, flipped a 3 wheeler and went sledding on a car hood and at no point did I ever and I mean ever have this much pain from an injury! Now I am couch ridden with the heating pad because I changed a lightbulb....you have got to be kidding me?! On top of this I gave my grandson a bath and when I drained the tub upstairs the water drained just fine but into the downstairs toilet! Now we have a drain issue and upon deep research we find that we need to find our septic tank!

A septic tank!

Not only do the garbage gods not haul off your refuse and the food gods fail to deliver to our new paradise but we also have to handle and store our own bathroom waste!

Picturing cousin Eddy on Vacation...."shitter's full"!

I remember when the trash man would come on Tuesdays by 7:10 weekly. The food delivery guys would drop off your warm, fried succulent goods within 10 minutes of hanging up the phone. When the kids would flush a washcloth or hotwheel car and it became the cities problem once you saw the swirl .....ahhh life was so easy back in the day.

Now Bob has to locate this wonderful box of all things waste so we can have someone come out and vacuum it clean like the housekeeping crew at at a toxic waste site. My house was starting to smell like a rest stop along a deserted interstate!

Bob finds the tomb of waste water and digs most of the day to locate the lid for the toilet calvary to arrive and rescue us from the septic nightmare.

Did I mention that it was 85 degrees today? In April? So now with my newfound injury I had to find ways to take care of a husband (because he does so well taking care of me), grandsons, my spoiled dog and the birds who help keep snakes out of my yard!

Instead of climbing the step ladder to replenish the bird feeder I opted to take a small tray and fill it with bird seed and place it on the coffee table on the deck for the birds to feed on. It was close to the feeder and it allowed our grandsons to watch them, that's a win, right?

So the birds are happy, my family is kept happy, life is good. The birds are so grateful to be fed they don't even make a mess of the deck, they get it, they really do.

Now I have had this same routine for a few days and Bob has grabbed the tray nightly to assure we keep the opossums at bay.

Tonight the Cardinals were playing and Bob actually was able to watch it online! Since moving here everything is all about SEC sports and we are ok with that but Bob needed a little MBL time in the recliner and he did perform hard labor most of the day. I figured it was getting late and I needed to get the tray off the deck. The dog was looking at me like an abused pup, he wanted to head up to bed so I decided to grab the tray and put the dog to bed. When I made it to the dining room with Dyme on my heels I grabbed the patio door handle and the outside light switch to shed light on my deck. What I did not expect to find sitting in my tray was a black mask wearing bandit feasting on my bird seed like he was noshing on the buffet at Golden Coral looking at me like I just caught him naked in my shower!

My very loud profanity laced scream should have brought my husband running to save me. The volume of both english and I think french profanity that I released should have sent him in the room with guns a blazing!

I was, however, met with......... "what's wrong?" from another freaking room! In the amount of time he spent uttering that simple question my hero could have been cocked and loaded, ready to defend me from whatever it was that had me screaming for dear life!

Apparently my cries for help were enough to make the mask wearing devil decide to make the right decision of fight or flight!

Now, when the invader has vacated the deck, my hero comes to investigate the situation!

The whole time Dyme (the dog) is crouched under the dining room table not even remotely ready to protect! I really need to rethink that whole spoiling dog thing on this cute little guy.

On to spring yard cleaning.....

Today my soulmate and I decided we would get the yard in order. Plenty of fall leaves still littered the yard and with the warmer weather coming in fast it was important to get the critter hiding spots cleared out. There are just too many creatures in this Ozark paradise that like to hideout until I get near them, no one else, just me.

Bob gets out the leaf blower and starts clearing all the corners. I get the broom and begin clearing off the porch and pulling down spider webs. The yard is coming along nicely. Bob heads over to the village of trash cans (no trash pick up, have to store the trash somewhere) and there are piles of leaves all around. Bob starts blowing the leaves into the hollar while I scrape wasp tunnels off the stone walls (I really hate insects of all varieties).

I hear Bob call my name from the side of the house closest to the hollar (go figure). I walk to the edge of the porch and ask him what he needs. I am met with "come here" but he is crouched down looking at the ground.

Nope, no way!

I respond with "what is it?".

Silence....

I yell this time "WHAT IS IT!?"

Bob tells me "just to come look" at something. This usually never ends well so I ask "is it a snake?".

Bob replies with "no it isn't a snake".

Ok, this is good so I ask "is it something else that is going to get me?"

Bob replies with "just come here, you have to see this".

My curiosity is definitely peaked, it isn't a snake and it can't get me what could possibly go wrong?

As I approach the area of intrigue Bob tells me to get close to him. When I reach his side and look down I am met with not one but two freaking snakes!

I scream and call him a liar as I back away plotting my revenge. Bob laughs and replies with "you asked if it was A SNAKE, I told you no. It is two snakes, I didn't lie".

I learned a valuable lesson in this outing.

Be clear when asking Bob questions and use both singular and plural forms of nouns in order for a correct response to be given.

In addition to that, plot better revenge scenarios because he is clearly not learning from them as yet!

He is blessed I let him live to see another day.

Bob and I decided we would have a small cookout with dad at lunch today. I put a couple steaks on the grill and one semi frozen chicken breast. I do not care for steak so I could get the kids fed while my chicken cooked. As I pulled the steaks off the grill I noticed the chicken needed more time so I threw some rolls in the oven. When it was time to pull the rolls I noticed the grill was engulfed in flames. The fire was shooting out of every crevice like I was filming the sequel to Backdraft on my back deck! I quickly ran to the deck and reached for the grill lid (not my best decision) and flung it open to release the fire gods that were dancing on my lunch. I was met with a lovely shade of charcoal and a lot of smoke. Let me just say, there is no sauce or condiment that can remove the taste of soot and propane from a very dead chicken.

So the diet starts today.....

After the lunch mess was cleaned up and dad headed home I decided on a little quiet time on the flame free deck. I sat down and watched as the birds came to feast and the bees flew through the deck like they were chasing lunch. Nature is calming when it doesn't involve medical attention.

I watched as a large carpenter bee landed on the table I was seated at. I wondered why they seemed to be so comfortable getting close to humans. Just as I was preparing to shoo it away a second one landed right next to the one currently enjoying my space.

This was either a very calculated attack or someone was going to die. You can only imagine my horror when bee 2 climbed on top of bee 1 and began getting his groove on in a very inappropriate (Marvin Gaye playing in the background) kind of way. On the very table we ate lunch at! These bees were doing the brown chicken, brown cow dance and did not mind an audience! My attempts to shoo them away completely ignored! Not only were they too busy to be bothered but they did not care that my vintage Wilson tennis racket was aimed and ready!

Well apparently I wasn't wearing the correct knee socks circa 1986 because I missed and the tribute to all things sex talk were able to finish!

I HAVE NEVER IN MY LIFE SEEN ANYTHING LIKE THIS AND PRAY I NEVER SEE IT AGAIN!

I am not sure why the creatures that surround me in this new paradise find it necessary to share their very public displays of affection.

I really think I need to stay inside a little more, maybe take up sewing. Anything to escape the triple x vibe going on outside my house!

I have come to the conclusion that my life from this point forward will never be boring. It will provide me with endless reasons to keep the Moscato market afloat.

My retirement and new found hormonal status will provide countless bits of crazy to share. The home we have grown to love will fuel endless chapters in this life of mine.

Life can't be lived unless someone unleashes the crazy.....

Acknowledgements

I could not have placed my life out there if it weren't for the push from my mother and father. Mom insisted I move forward with this venture and was positive I would be famous (makes me smile).

My one regret, she did not see my book go to print. She read my very first book and loved it, so for that I am thankful.

My husband who is my hero (most of the time), my grandsons and my family all of whom made everything on these pages happen.

Life can be a magnificent ride or a series of unfortunate events, it's what you take from it that makes your journey worth it.

Made in the USA
Las Vegas, NV
28 January 2022